Presented in grateful appreciation to

MR. & MRS. GEORGE LYNN

*And he said: "I tell you the truth, unless you
change and become like little children, you
will never enter the kingdom of heaven."
(Matthew 18:3)*

For the child in you, and the children you share
this with, I offer the blessings favored through
the birth of the Child sent to save the world,
our Lord, Jesus Christ.

+ Joseph A. Galante

Most Reverend Joseph A. Galante, D.D., J.C.D
Bishop of Camden

Christmas 2010

St. Cecilia's Orchestra

Art by Michael O'Neill McGrath
Poetry by Alan J. Hommerding

Photograph by Carl J Krzystofczyk, copyright © Carl J Krzystofczyk.
Used by permission.

The paintings were done in acrylics on watercolor paper.

This book was edited by Christine Krzystofczyk with assistance
from Marcia T. Lucey. Design and layout by Christine Enault.
Production manager was Deb Johnston. The book was set in Fritz Quadrata.
Printed in the United States. Graphics TwoFortyFour Inc.

WLP 017348   ISBN 978-1-58459-475-8

Read This
BOOK
ALOUD!

ffffffffffffffffffffff

Listen for the Music
in the Words.

St. Cecilia's Orchestra

Michael O'Neill McGrath, OSFS
and
Alan J. Hommerding

WORLD LIBRARY PUBLICATIONS
Franklin Park, Illinois

On her celestial podium
Cecilia stands and listens.
What sweet, melodic sound she hears,
Both near and in the distance.

How beautiful this music is,
Just like a symphony!
How great this gift creation has
To praise God's majesty.

"I'll make an orchestra!" she cries,
"It is my sacred duty
To hear each prrum-pum, plink and plunk,
The chings and root-toot-tooties!"

So off she sails upon the wind,
The Holy Spirit's wings,
From star to cloud, from hill to shore,
To hear more wondrous things.

Come join Cecilia's holy quest,
Take part in this, her story,
And through the Holy Spirit hear
The sounds that give God glory.

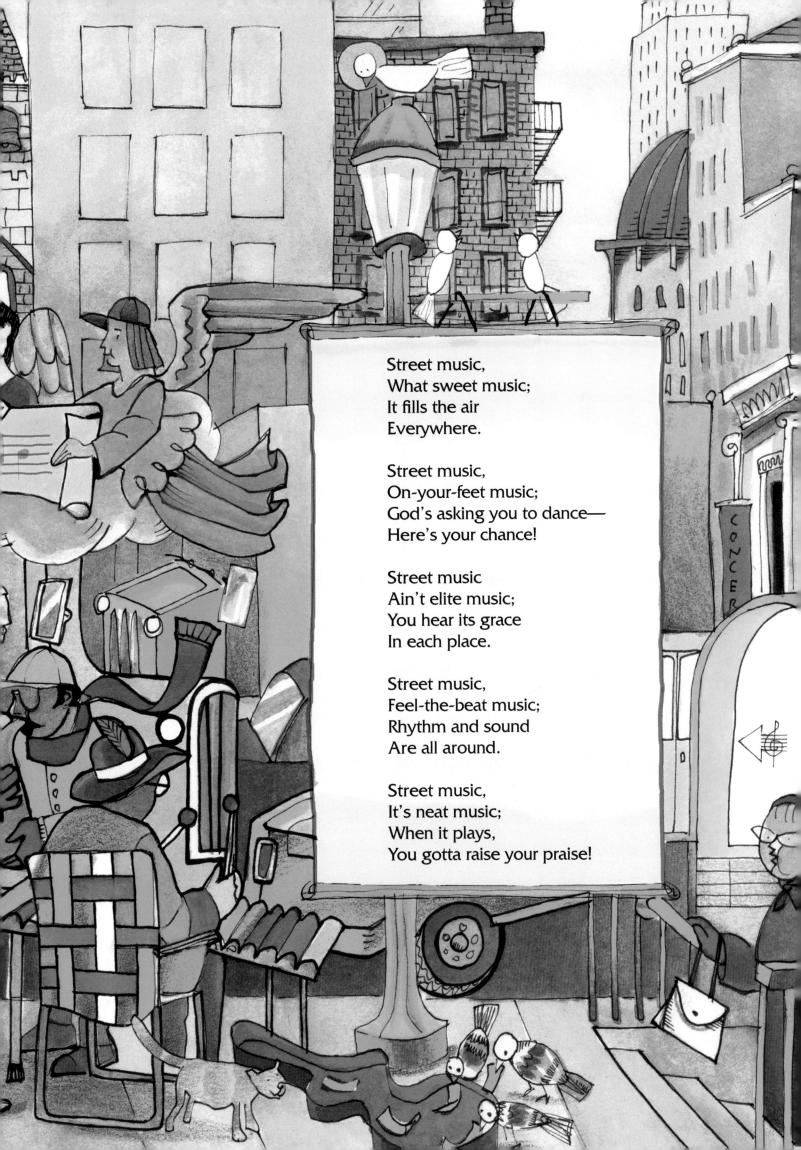

Street music,
What sweet music;
It fills the air
Everywhere.

Street music,
On-your-feet music;
God's asking you to dance—
Here's your chance!

Street music
Ain't elite music;
You hear its grace
In each place.

Street music,
Feel-the-beat music;
Rhythm and sound
Are all around.

Street music,
It's neat music;
When it plays,
You gotta raise your praise!

A mighty, mighty wind
Once swept across the sea;
The Sea of Reeds became dry land,
God's people were set free!

That wind still blows today,
Mysterious and warm,
Through clarinets and saxophones,
Through zurnas, oboes, shawms.

Hear the reeds
Shout God's deeds!

FEEL the steady, sonic heartbeat,
REAL as heaven's pulsing life,
STEEL and string and wood together
KNEEL to pray and worship God!

TAKE the grass harp, soft and tender;
SHAKE the gourds of different kinds;
MAKE resounding tones, kalimba;
WAKE the mellow balafon!

STRUM and pluck the joyful kora,
DRUM the djembe mightily!
FROM Algeria to Zimbabwe
COME from every tribe and land:

BRING the gifts of all the nations,
RING your music out in praise,
SPRING up, dance and clap in rhythm,
FLING your spirits open wide!

Harold is an angel
From the holy throng
Who raised their glorious song
Over Bethlehem.

Hark! His name reminds us
Of that blessed morn
When Jesus Christ was born,
Savior of the world.

Harold has a trumpet
For a future time,
A morning made sublime
With eternal light.

Practicing with passion,
Is his way to pray
Until that splendid day
Christ will come again!

We, like angel Harold,
Always must prepare
For that trumpet's blare
Sounding heaven's call.

Oh, the peal, peal, pealing
Of the lustrous, golden bells!
Played with care and flair and feeling,
Hear them carol on—free-wheeling:
How their charming chiming swells!

Heaven's bliss and grace and healing
Tolling from the tower, tells
Times for prayer, God's love revealing—
From the floor up to the ceiling—
How appealing!
Ring the bells!

Electric, acoustic, twelve-string, bass ●
Built in many different sizes or shapes; ●
Guitars, by nimble fingers and thumbs ●
Delight our spirits with every strum! ●
All of them help us hear God's grace: ●
Electric, acoustic, twelve-string, bass! ●

What does heaven sound like?
How do we hear it here,
Its gentle, healing presence,
Its light so strong and clear?

The harp's celestial echoes
Come forth from many strands,
With graceful tones arising,
Caressed by angel hands.

Both earth and
    heaven's music
Are heard when it is played;
And all of us, in rapture,
Know a saintly serenade.

Hu-ROO!
Hu-ROO!
Who can play
the didgeridoo?
Can you?
Could a
kangaroo?

Hooray!
Hooray!
Its ancient tone
Calls us to pray!

So,
don't be fidgety.
Pray, and play
the didgeridoo,
every didgeri-day!

What is wooden, stone, or clay?
Made of silver, gold, or tin?
What is known the whole world over,
Longer, shorter, round, and thin?

Flutes are all this and much more.
Their spinning, soaring, supple tone
Fleetly floats and flies aloft,
Wafting, whirling round God's throne.

The ram's horn echoed long ago
From Sinai's holy heights,
Proclaiming days of festival
With shivery delight!

At *Rosh Ha-shana,*
    new year's time,
It still rings forth today,
The Rabbi chants, *Tokea* blasts,
And all are called to pray.

Tekiah is one way it blares,
Another, *shevarim.*
Teruah is a final shout;
Each one a sound supreme.

O hear this ancient, startling cry,
This roar so loud and clear,
A sign that God does something new,
A signal all can hear!

BRASS BAND!!!

It's a band!
It's a band!
It's a big brass band!
Hear the bright and bracing sound—
Give them a cheer!
Give them a hand!

The bugle calls tah-TAH-tah-TAH,
The horn curls upside down:
Give them a smile,
No one can frown at a big brass band!

Look out! Here comes the slippery slide
Of the big trombone—
Is that a tuba in the back?
No, it's a sousaphone in the big brass band!

Join the band!
  Join the band!
    What a happy jamboree,
      What a heavenly jubilee:
        Saints and angels, you and me,
          All parade in harmony with the
          BIG
            BRASS
              BAND!

Its name means "soft"
But it's real proud
To play quite loud
And please a crowd.

Not in a park,
A bench is there.
(Care to share?
It seats a pair!)

There is no lock,
But lots of keys—
Eighty-eight, please—
Lead hymns with ease.

It's not a fish
Yet scales abound,
Going up, going down,
Around and around.

There's white and black,
But folks of all hues
Choose its muse
To spread the Good News!

And your piano?
Grand or little,
Certainly it'll
Solve these riddles!

mystery divine
worship-bearing hallowed strings
quiver jubilant

godly wonderment
spirit-rousing sacred bells
glitter around us

godly majesty
temple-filling blessed gong
showers halo light

harmony divine
beauty-making peoples all
savor godly prayer

Whenever saints must place a call
That goes from cloud to cloud,
They make the call on aerophones—
These aerophones are LOUD!

St. Margaret, on her bagpipes, calls
From Scotland, cool and dewy;
In France, she's answered on musette:
Who is it? It's St. Louis!

St. Catherine on her pifa plays
In sunny Italy;
Elizabeth her duda trills
On hills of Hungary.

Augustine makes the zukra zing
O'er wide Egyptian plains;
Ignatius basks on mountains high;
His basque-pipes call from Spain.

No busy signals on their lines,
Though saints are always home;
So if you want to call them up,
Pick up your aerophone!

"My, how you've grown!" they'd say to me
When I was just a girl.
Now here I am, God's holy saint,
And known around the world.

My, how the organ's pipes have swelled
From small and few to grand;
How nobly it can elevate
The song of many lands.

At first it would not be allowed—
When it was a wee thing—
In places that the Christians came
To worship, pray, and sing.

But organ pipes could grow and change,
And so could people's hearts,
So organists, with hands (and feet!)
Now help it play its part.

The "King of Instruments" it's crowned,
It makes orchestral thunder;
And also, still and soft, it shows us
Heaven's joy and wonder.

Shake it up! Stir it up!
Turn up the heat!
Praise God with music that's
Spicy and sweet!

Conga drums, marimba,
Güirro, maracas—
Get your ear set to hear
A flavorful salsa!

Strum, mariachi,
Pluck the grand guittarón;
Top it off—merengue!—
Pray on and on.

Latin America
Gives us the beat:
¡Olé! Hallelujah,
A musical treat!

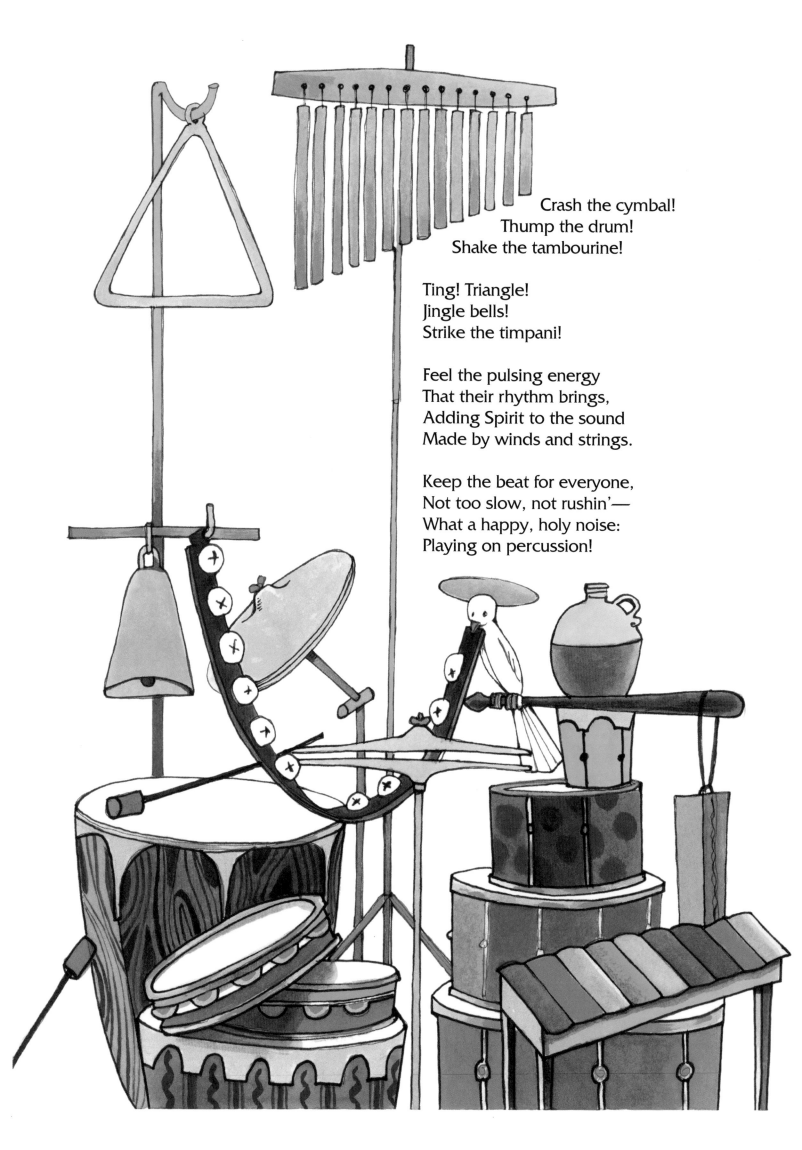

Crash the cymbal!
Thump the drum!
Shake the tambourine!

Ting! Triangle!
Jingle bells!
Strike the timpani!

Feel the pulsing energy
That their rhythm brings,
Adding Spirit to the sound
Made by winds and strings.

Keep the beat for everyone,
Not too slow, not rushin'—
What a happy, holy noise:
Playing on percussion!

BALALAIKA
BALALAIKA

Oh
nothing thrills the air
like a balalaika,
like a balalaika!

So
shimmering and rare,
sounding plinka-plaika,
sounding plinka-plaika!

Now
listen to it soar
like our prayers arise,
like our prayers arise!

In
worship evermore
filling paradise,
filling paradise!

With the balalaika
And its plinka-plaika
Let your prayers arise
Up to paradise!

A violinist warming up alone
Is playing SOLO;
Another comes to fiddle 'round
And then you have a DUO.

Viola's next, with dulcet tone.
Voilà! you have a TRIO:
Want to guess
  what happens next,
When you add the cello?

What's it called
  when there are four?
Care to make a bet?
You would win
  if you replied,
"You'd have a
  string quartet."

The string bass adds the lowest tones.
Five players? Here's a hint:
As all of them
   come into place,
The "et" you have
   is "quint!"

The players, bows in hand, tune up—
Much more than six or seven—
To lead, in beauty's holiness,
The symphony of heaven.

So St. Cecilia noted all
        These instruments, and more.
    She listened well
            to know which ones
                Could worship and adore.

    What did she hear,
        while traveling
            To all these different places?
            Why, EVERY kind
                of instrument
                Can offer sacred praises!

God named each one
  (like you and me),
Gave each a job to do:
To share the music of God's love
With sounds both old and new.

But there can be no orchestra
Without someone to play
The holy instruments God made
So we, through them, can pray.

Cecilia, with the Spirit near,
Now raises her baton . . .
So raise your instrument as well,
Come join her, everyone!

Michael (Mickey) O'Neill McGrath

Brother Mickey McGrath is an Oblate of St. Francis de Sales who lives and works in Camden, New Jersey—when he is not on the road giving retreats and presentations on art and faith. He has received awards from Catholic Press Association for four books and for covers of *America* magazine. Mickey's work appears regularly in the publications of today's leading Catholic and Christian publishers.

St. Cecilia's Orchestra is his fifth book for World Library Publications, and his third specifically for children. (His other children's books are *Jesus A to Z* and *Mysteries of the Rosary*.) He holds a Master of Fine Arts degree in painting from American University in Washington, D.C., but has loved to draw and paint ever since he can remember.

It was a pleasure and an honor to work on *St. Cecilia's Orchestra* because even though I am not a musician myself, I grew up in a family of music lovers. My father loved classical music and opera, my mother loved Broadway and easy listening music, and my brothers and sisters and I loved pop and rock. For me there is also the music of the Church, especially chant, and the piano, organ, and vocal work of too many dear friends to mention by name. I had all these loves to ponder as I worked on the paintings for this book. This is for them.

St. Cecilia has been a popular subject in art for many centuries. I have painted many other images of St. Cecilia over the years, in various guises and styles, and even visited her home and tomb in Rome in preparation for this project. I hope you can agree that the special prayers I made there for Alan, myself, and our team of editors were answered: prayers for a fun book that would inspire you to make some beautiful noise to God.

A special highlight for me was being permitted to observe a rehearsal of the Philadelphia Chamber Orchestra under the direction of Maestro Ignat Solzhenitsyn at the Kimmel Center in Philadelphia. I did pages and pages of sketches that eventually became the one drawing of the stringed instruments at the end. So thank you, Maestro! *Bravo!*

Bravo also to Alan, Chris Krzystofczyk, and the entire team at WLP!

And *molti bravi* to you, the reader.

Alan J. Hommerding

Alan J. Hommerding is Senior Liturgy Publications Editor at World Library Publications. He holds graduate degrees in theology, liturgy, and music from St. Mary's Seminary and University, Baltimore, and the University of Notre Dame.

Alan is the editor of *AIM: Liturgy Resources*, WLP's quarterly liturgy and music magazine. He is the composer of numerous choral octavos, and contributed to the *ChicAGO Centenary Organ Anthology*. He is the author of many hymn texts, some of which appear in his hymnary *Song of the Spirit*. As a hymn text author he appears in *Panorama of Christian Hymnody* and the *New Cambridge Dictionary of Hymnology*. He is the author of *Blessed Are the Music-Makers, Words That Work for Worship, In Holy Harmony,* and *Everyday Psalms: 150 Meditations for Living the Lord's Songs,* and compiled *A Sourcebook about Music* for Liturgy Training Publications.

He is a member of the music advisory staff for the Archdiocese of Chicago's Office for Divine Worship, and a member of the music ministry staff at St. Joseph Parish in Downers Grove, Illinois.

I hope everyone enjoys reading these poems as much as I enjoyed writing them. As it says at the beginning of the book, it is important to read these poems aloud. Doing so will add to the enjoyment. You can come back to the poems many times: try reading them a bit slower or faster, emphasizing different words, hearing things you didn't the first time. See if you can discover different poetic devices that were used. Here are a few, just to get you started:

• The poem about African instruments uses *head* rhyme: the rhyming word appears at the beginning, not the end, of each line—so you have to listen and read it aloud a bit differently.

• The guitar poem is an *acrostic*: the first letter of each line spells something (in this case it "spells" the pitch names of the guitar's six strings).

• The poem for the Asian instruments uses *haiku*: a Japanese form in which seventeen syllables are divided five-seven-five.

Some of the poems might have the names of instruments you may not be familiar with. (Do you know what a balafon is?) Any dictionary or encyclopedia will help you learn about them.

Like Saint Cecilia, you have to be ready to explore and listen with the Holy Spirit. Enjoy!

Saint Cecilia

Saint Cecilia has long been honored as the patron saint of music. She was martyred for being a Christian, but the life of Christ that was in her from her baptism continued on. Stories of her life that spread after her death told how, as she was being martyred, she sang hymns of praise to God. The pope at the time, Urbanus I, placed her body in a place of honor alongside some early bishops.

Saint Cecilia is one of only a few women named in the official prayers of the Roman Catholic Mass. One of the prayers for her feast day mentioned the organ (or "the pipes"), which is why she is often pictured with a small pipe organ. The pipe organ and her martyr's crown are the two symbols most often shown with her.

Many stained glass windows feature Saint Cecilia surrounded by a heavenly orchestra of angels playing a variety of instruments. Poets have written long poems called "odes" in her honor, and some famous composers set them to music so people could sing about music and Saint Cecilia.

A large church in Rome is named for her. It was built on the ruins of a temple of a Roman goddess of light and vision, and Cecilia's name is often translated as "way for the blind." Some scholars think that the property where the church is located once belonged to Saint Cecilia's family. To this day, many Roman Catholic churches are named in her honor. Her feast day is November 22.